DEDIC.

WI

SHAYLYN

I'LL ALWAYS BE HERE TO PICK YOU UP WHEN YOU FALL DOWN
AND REMIND YOU THAT YOU CAN DO ANYTHING YOU PUT YOUR
MIND TO. I HOPE TO BE THE PARENT THAT YOUR GRANDMA AND
GRANDPA WERE TO ME AND HELP YOU LIVE OUT ALL YOUR
DREAMS AND ASPIRATIONS.

"DREAM BIG LITTLE BUNNY, ANYTHING CAN BE ACHIEVED!"

THERE WAS A BUNNY
WHO LOVED TO PLAY

BUT SO MANY PEOPLE
HAD THEIR SAY

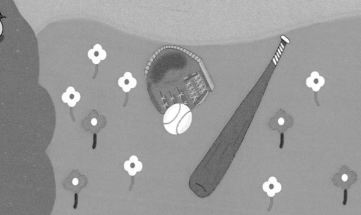

YOU CAN'T DO THIS
YOU CAN'T DO THAT

YOU'RE TOO BIG, TOO SMALL,
TOO YOUNG TO BAT

THE LITTLE BUNNY
RAN AWAY

ALL I WANT TO DO
IS PLAY

I'LL GO INSIDE
AND THERE I'LL STAY

MAYBE THEN I'LL
GET MY SAY

ALL COOPED UP
IS NOT MUCH FUN

WHEN LITTLE BUNNY
JUST WANTS TO RUN

SAD AND BORED
WITH TIME TO THINK

OF ALL THE FUN
MISSED AT THE RINK

COME HERE CHILD
LET'S TALK THIS OUT

WHAT'S THE LONG FACE
ALL ABOUT?

IF IT WERE UP TO ME
I'D PLAY AND PLAY

I'D RUN AND JUMP
AND SWING ALL DAY

BUT WHEN I PLAY
THEY STOP AND STARE

WHY DO THEY JUDGE ME
IT'S JUST NOT FAIR

I'M TOO TALL, TOO SHORT, TOO YOUNG TO PLAY

THAT'S WHAT EVERYONE HAS TO SAY

THEY SAY I'M NOT GOOD
ENOUGH TO PLAY

BUT I'D PLAY ALL DAY
IF I HAD IT MY WAY

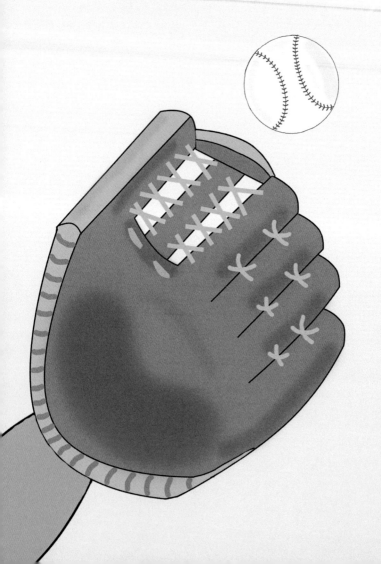

COME HERE LOVE
AND LISTEN CLOSE

I'LL TELL YOU WHAT'S IMPORTANT
WHAT MATTERS MOST

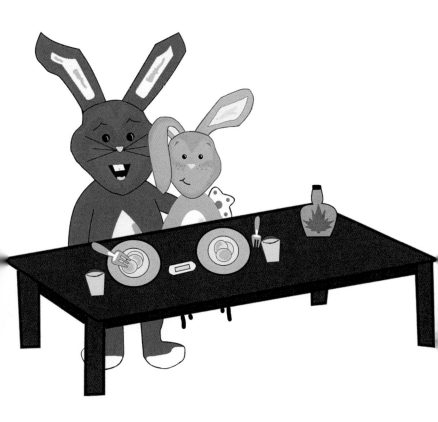

YOU'RE NOT TOO TALL, TOO SHORT – JUST RIGHT

PLAY YOUR HEART OUT AND YOU'LL SHINE BRIGHT

PICK UP THAT TWIG
AND HAVE SOME FUN

IT'S NOT ABOUT THE SCORE
WHO'S LOST OR WON

YOU'RE THE ONE WHO
SHOULD HAVE THE SAY

IN WHAT GAMES AND
ACTIVITIES YOU PLAY PLAY PLAY!

SO GET OUT THERE
AND GET IT DONE

BUT MOST IMPORTANTLY

HAVE SOME <u>FUN!</u>

SO ON AND ON
THE BUNNY PLAYED

THIS LOVE FOR SPORTS
WILL NEVER FADE

THE LESSONS LEARNED
CAN'T BE BOUGHT

IT'S MUCH MORE
THAN YOU'RE EVER TAUGHT

IT'LL TAKE YOU PLACES YOU'D NEVER GO

TEACH YOU THINGS YOU'D NEVER KNOW

DON'T UNDERESTIMATE
THE POWER OF PLAY

THIS BUNNY WILL GROW
AND LEARN EACH DAY

LITTLE BUNNY IS NOW BIG
AND STRONG THEY SAY

ALL FROM THE LOVE
AND JOY OF PLAY

**WHAT MATTERS MOST
IS WHAT <u>YOU</u> BELIEVE**

**DREAM BIG LITTLE BUNNY
ANYTHING CAN BE ACHIEVED!**

Manufactured by Amazon.ca
Bolton, ON